G000109591

Farming with Steam

HAROLD BONNETT

Shire Publications Ltd.

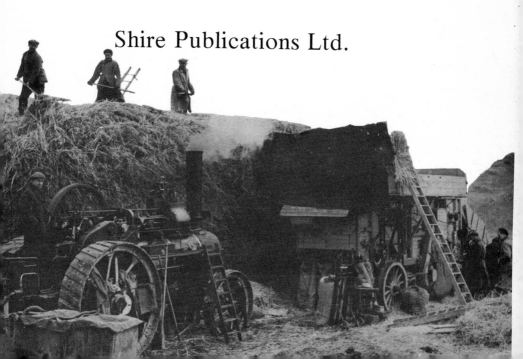

2

ISBN 0 85263 285 1
Library of Congress Catalog Card Number: 74-83351

(Previous page) *Mr Carter the farmer, his threshing gang and the 1922 Ruston (Lincoln) engine had threshed like this for many a year at Deeping St Nicholas in south Lincolnshire. This 1952 photograph shows how loth they were to change over to the new order of combine harvesters. The overcoated men and the tarpaulin wind-shield on the drum speak plainly of a bitingly cold winter wind blowing across the exposed fenland. Note the folded sack under a weight on the weighing machine to compensate for the weight of a sack.*

The cover design by Ron Shaddock shows: (top) *Wallis & Steevens 3 tons 6 cwt steam tractor pulling a corn binder about 1907;* (below) *Société Français portable threshing oats in 1912.*

Contents

(Below) *John Fowler mole drainer implement.*

PHOTOGRAPHIC ACKNOWLEDGEMENTS

Photographs are acknowledged as follows: John H. Boughton Collection, 62; Art Dickey Collection, 27; Herr Friedrich Fischer, 93, 94; Fodens Ltd, 75; Bob Gibbons Collection, 25; Glenbow-Alberta Institute, 34, 51; Mr Bill Harmston, 81; Mr F. Hal Higgins, 89; Kodak Museum, 5; Museum of English Rural Life, 6, 7, 9, 10, 11, 16, 28, 31, 35, 37, 39, 73, 74, 77, 79; National Traction Engine Club journal, *Steaming*, 48, 49; National Traction Engine Club publication, *Engines at Work*, 65; *Northampton Evening Press*, page 1; Mr R. G. Pratt, 86; R. L. S. Journal, 12, 29, 43; R. L. S. Photographic Section, 1, 13, 26, 30, 52, 61, 91; Mr John Russell, 90; Lewis Sommerfield Collection, cover (top), 18, 21, 24, 33, 44, 47, 80; Stretham Engine Trust 2, 3, 4; Mr Cyril Broughton, 68, 71; Mr George Hughes, 14, 59; Mr Bob Linton, 69, 85; Mr Derek Petty, 60; Mr Ben Taylor, 32.

1. *This Lincoln-built William Foster & Co. threshing engine No 2163, now only partly employed, had in the ownership of Chatterton & Cooke threshed through many a hard long day in south Lincolnshire. It is seen here at Deeping St Nicholas. Threshing was not done in the rain and few threshing engines had a canopy like this one.*

Introduction

The steam engine played a varied and glorious part in the realm of agriculture, beginning in the early nineteenth century with the introduction of steam pumping engines to drain the Fenland marshes, and reaching its peak with the magnificent steam ploughs and threshing machines of the latter part of Victoria's reign and the early years of the twentieth century, but declining in the face of competition from the petrol-driven tractor after the First World War. The steam engine gave sterling service to farmers and it is hoped that the photographs and text in this book will convey some impression of those grand old days of steam on the farm.

The steam engine on the farm certainly produced a special race of men. They were men who never minded hard work, nor long hours and often rough modes of living. They were also outstandingly self-sufficient, managing to get by with success under the most trying of conditions. The men also liked their engines and this usually made their work a pleasure to them. Confirmation of all this is abundantly clear whenever one gets into conversation with an old threshing-engine driver, or a member of an old-time steam cultivation gang. More often than not these men say, 'Those were the happiest days of my life.'

As most of the engines illustrated in this book have their power rating described in nominal horse power (n.h.p.), the use of this term may need an explanation. When the first farm engines were made in the 1840s, their makers listed them as being able to displace this or that number of horses for working threshing machines. Their reckonings fell well below the properly calculated horsepower, but the power rating stuck. Multiply the stated nominal horse power by nine and this will give you an acceptable figure of the actual or indicated horse power of any engine.

The photograph on page 1 was taken on 17th February 1952, and the *Northampton Evening Press* said about it: 'A farmyard threshing scene where the old order still prevails in face of overwhelming competition by tractors and combine harvesters. On Mr Carter's farm faith is not broken with a loyal servant, a stalwart Ruston & Hornsby traction engine which is in its thirty-first season.' But it was almost the time of goodbye.

Farming with Steam

LAND DRAINAGE

It was the Scottish-born engineer James Watt (1736-1819) who, by improving upon the beam engines of earlier British engineers, gave us the first steam engines that could be harnessed to an agricultural use. From 1818 Watt's design of beam engine and similar Cornish-type engines of low pressure and slow-working characteristics were used for land drainage. They were ideal as helpmeets or substitutes for the seven hundred or so windmills which were then used to lift surplus water from the often flooded Fenlands around the Wash, mainly in the counties of Cambridgeshire and Lincolnshire. Here was some of the most fertile farmland in Britain, but it depended almost entirely upon artificial drainage, especially in spring just before crop-planting time. Windmill power was unreliable, because very often there was no wind at all after heavy rains or as snow thawed, which were just the times when the floodwaters inundated the flat countryside.

These Fenlands were sectioned off into districts controlled by drainage commissioners and it was the Waterbeach Level Commissioners who erected the steam pumping station at Stretham near Ely (plates 2, 3, 4). They recovered their costs from drainage rates levied upon the farmers under their jurisdiction. The very first steam pump was installed in 1818 at Sutton St Edmunds between Wisbech and Spalding, and there were nine other steam engines in Fenland use when the Stretham engine started its work. All the heavy machinery, made by the Butterley Company of Ripley in Derbyshire, would have had to be transported by water. The first stage would have been down the river Trent to the Humber, then out to sea

---

2. (Top left) *Stretham Old Engine House still contains the Butterley Company's 1831 beam engine that pumped water from the fen behind it into the old course of the river Ouse in the foreground.*

3. (Far left) *The 37ft scoop wheel of the Stretham engine.*

4. (Near left) *The top of the 8ft long and 3ft 3in diameter cylinder of the Stretham engine.*

round the coast of Lincolnshire to King's Lynn, and finally up the winding course of the river Ouse to Stretham just above Ely. Or alternatively, a short cut may have been taken by using the Roman-dug Foss Dyke canal from the Trent at Torksey to the Witham at Lincoln and thence down to Boston for the crossing of the Wash.

The water-lifting steam engine played a very great part in transforming the soggy wastes of Fenland into farmland of the highest quality. Much had been done in former times, strengthening the river banks, or cutting direct water-catchment drains, but it was not until the advent of the steam engine that satisfactory drainage was accomplished. It is recorded that in 1840 the use of steam pumps in the Lincolnshire Fens had pushed up the value of land from £20 to £70 an acre.

FARM STEAM ENGINES ON WHEELS

A unique engine for cable-style ploughing was built as early as 1834 by John Heathcoat MP and Josiah Parkes; it moved about on caterpillar tracks and was not a great success.

In the 1840s, prompted by one or two of their more progressively minded farmer customers, several old-established agricultural engineering firms, such as Tuxford's of Boston or Ransome & May of Ipswich, tried their hand at building what were called portable steam engines. Examples of improved portable engines of a later period are illustrated in plates 9 and 16. As their name implies, these engines were not self-moving and it was necessary to use either bullocks or horses to move them from one job to the next. The main tasks given to these engines were one-engine roundabout-style cultivation, threshing, corn milling, chaff cutting, and other odd jobs where their flywheels were coupled by a leather belt to the machinery.

John Fowler, pioneer of the steam plough, achieved his first success in 1856 at Nacton in Suffolk. He used a portable steam engine to power a rope windlass by which the plough was pulled to and fro across the field. The fact that an acre an hour was ploughed that day made it a notable occasion in the history of mechanised farming in Britain. The traction-type plough engines shown in plates 6 and 8 represent Fowler's later ideas for doing the same job with self-moving engines.

5. (Right) *An 1854 photograph of a small pumping engine of the table type, standing on a graceful four-legged iron table. It was probably made by William Tuxford & Sons of Boston, who made their first agricultural steam engine as early as 1842. The scene is the tidal Nene near Wisbech, where the engine is either pumping or pile-driving during embankment repairs. Tuxfords installed similar engines in the Lincolnshire fens.*

6. (Above) *Cable-type ploughing in 1862. This photograph shows John Fowler's method, using one engine, a balance plough and a rope anchor cart. The elegant two-cylinder engine, with ideally broad-rimmed wheels, was made by Kitson & Hewitson of Leeds.*

7. (Right) *Farmer Benjamin Bomford of Pitchill, Warwickshire, sits on one of a pair of plough engines made for him in 1864 by W. Savory & Son, High Orchard Iron Works, Gloucester. This type of cable-style plough engine, whilst natty in appearance, did not prove popular.*

The impact that the appearance of these first steam engines made upon rural communities must have been very great indeed. Countrymen were, of course, already acquainted with the machinery of windmills and watermills, as well as with that of hand or horse-driven threshing machines, but for all that it was certainly something of note when a portable steam engine came and made its home in a remote village.

This was the time, too, that the coal-fired steam engine began to relieve mankind of some of his more arduous labours and showed the first faint green light along the road towards the present leisured days.

STEAM CULTIVATION

There is no doubt at all about the claim that steam made a real name for itself on land cultivation work. The steam plough put British farmers into a position where the whole world envied their splendid crop-raising

8. *John Fowler double drum plough engine No 814 (1867), intended for one-engine ploughing. One rope drum pulled the plough outwards to the anchor cart and the rope on the other drum pulled it back again. A set of speed governors was provided to enable the engine to be used for belt work. One hand lever was the reverser and the other changed the drive to the drums. As the steerage is linked to the rear wheels, this engine probably ran tender first.*

capacities. The great power of the steam engine meant that land could now be ploughed or cultivated sufficiently deeply, not only to provide deeper tilth for plant roots, but also for rooting up difficult weeds like twitch, docks or thistles and killing them during the tillage of summer fallows. In this respect, especially on the heavy clays of eastern England, the steam plough gave a great boost to our farming.

Before 1860 one-engine or roundabout tackles, using cable haulage in conjunction with fixed or movable windlasses, predominated in England. But in the 1860s John Fowler began turning out from his newly founded Steam Plough Works at Hunslet in Leeds rope-drum fitted traction engines that worked in pairs with one engine on either side of the field. This cable system, incorporating a pair of mobile engines that could tackle irregularly shaped fields, and able also to move themselves from field to field, from farm to farm, or from village to village, was an immediate success in Britain. Right from the start it was obvious that the best way of using these expensive tackles was for them to be owned and worked by steam cultivation contractors, with the farmer paying an acreage charge for the work done and additionally finding the coal and water for the engines. Two-engine cable ploughing quickly established itself and by 1900 there were around six hundred of these tackles at work in Great Britain. The two main tools used were the balance plough and the heavy-tined cultivator. These British steam-plough sets ploughed, cultivated, harrowed or mole-drained over a million acres of ground annually, and they did their work well.

Unlike threshing, which went on throughout the winter months, steam cultivation usually ceased from about November until the following March or April. The big plough engines, weighing between twelve and eighteen tons each, were far too heavy to flounder about on the soft wet fields in winter.

PLOUGH-ENGINE DESIGN

At first Fowler's plough engines of the 1860s had two simple-acting cylinders placed side by side over the firebox end of the boiler. This meant that the crankshaft and the flywheel were at the front or chimney end, as

9. *Ransome Sims & Jeffries (Ipswich) portable engine driving a corn mill, about 1880: a demonstration showing how corn could be ground into animal feed or flour on the farm by using power from the threshing engine. The belt is round the engine's smaller flywheel because the grinding mill turned relatively slowly. Spare grindstones are carried on the two-wheeled cart.*

also was the bevel shaft drive to the hind wheels. A big change made in the middle 1860s was the building of single-cylinder engines with their cylinder block at the front and the crankshaft at the rear, setting a trend that was never reversed. These single-cylinder engines were, in their day, a great success for they were powerful and durable machines known just as 'singles' to steam-ploughmen. Their main fault was that they used an awful lot of coal and water. The British market was so flooded with these tough old engines that would not wear out, that although Fowlers introduced compound plough engines in the early 1880s, very few of the latter were sold into the British market for another thirty years.

Compound engines use their steam twice over, first in a small high-pressure cylinder and then in the second-stage, larger, low-pressure cylinder. These compounds were more economical than the singles, and since the farmer had to buy all the coal and cart all the water, he was naturally interested in hiring a contractor who was equipped with compound engines, especially after about 1917 when the price of coal started to go up alarmingly. Neither was water an insignificant feature, for a set of the loud-exhausting singles needed watering almost two hourly when cultivating on hard-baked clay land in summer. The farmer's man had to pump all the water into the water-cart, using the streams, ponds or rivers nearest to the working engines, and often he was hard pressed to keep the set at work without irritating breaks waiting for water. As an encouragement to keep them well supplied with water, the steam-ploughmen often gave the water-cart man a daily tip of a shilling or so.

The peak of Fowler's plough-engine design is represented in the eighteen-ton 16 n.h.p. BB class compounds that appeared from about 1913, and the 18 n.h.p. AA class compounds of a year or so later. It was engines of these types that both the men and the farmers liked to have around. For beauty of appearance the BB class can scarcely be beaten by any traction engine, and it is a lovely engine to handle. The Aveling & Porter plough engine shown in plate 71 is certainly a good-looking compound but, all in all, there was nothing to beat a Fowler plough engine for appearance or for performance.

DIRECT-TRACTION PLOUGHING

There were some steam engines that did their work hitched in front of the plough, doing what was known as direct traction work. It had been hoped from the very beginning to do steam cultivation in this simple manner, but due chiefly to the heavy weight of all steam engines in relation to their power output, the method never succeeded on the soft, damp soils of Great Britain. Nevertheless hope died hard in the hearts and minds of many quite clever steam designers, and many years elapsed

10. *8 n.h.p. Ransome 'Colonist' road steamer. Here is an unusual steam engine helping a gardener rather than a farmer, for it is engaged in transporting a largish tree in 1872 for transplantation in the garden of Mr R. C. Ransome of Ipswich. Poor steaming was a troublesome feature of the rather ugly pot boiler on these engines, and in this instance the fireman can be seen anxiously looking up at his steam gauge.*

before the final disappointment. Plate 30 gives a general idea what direct ploughing looked like under English conditions when using a light steam tractor. In America and other countries with drier soils it was the rule for the engine to pull the plough.

It was the appearance of oil-engined farm tractors about 1909 that really disconcerted many British traction-engine builders. The immediate reaction was to spur their designers on towards producing several cleverly conceived lightweight steam engines. Unfortunately it was a forlorn hope, not only for engines intended to do direct ploughing, but also for those steam engines which were tried out in the hayfield and in the harvest field. The engines were perfectly capable of doing these tasks, but it was just as cheap and probably handier to use horses.

When a steam engine was ploughing by the direct method, it required thirty to fifty per cent of the available power to move the engine alone, so it was clearly uneconomic to work this way.

WARD & DALE LTD OF SLEAFORD

What is now to the world but a name was to me as a boy, and to many others as well, an emotional èxpression. For the firm of Ward & Dale Ltd, the largest of all steam cultivation contractors, had a fleet of twenty-four two-engine sets of superbly organised and operated John Fowler steam ploughs. Every farmhand within twenty miles of Sleaford in Lincolnshire knew about Ward & Dale. The 1910 photograph shown in plate 50 enables us to take a look back at some of the firm's engines and men just before they started that season's work.

This firm, which was operating in the late 1870s, was formed by two gentlemen farmers named Ward, who found the money, and Billy Dale, who brought with him the practical knowledge of ploughing by steam.

Each cultivating set had a crew of five: a foreman in charge, two engine-drivers, a ploughman and a cook boy. A four-wheeled wooden living van, which served as a cookhouse and five-bunk sleeping place, travelled around with each pair of engines. In March the tackles rolled noisily out of Sleaford to begin work all over south Lincolnshire, and even further afield into parts of Nottinghamshire, Rutland and North-amptonshire. A five-furrow plough and an eleven or thirteen-tine cultivator, as well as a two-wheeled 250 gallon water-cart, completed the equipment of each set. The men went home either once a week or fortnightly; but the engines and tackle stayed out until mid November when the fields had become too wet and sticky for steam work.

Hard work and long hours were the willingly accepted lot of these steam-ploughmen whose efforts in the field were encouraged by a bonus, or acreage payment, of a few pence to each man for every acre ploughed. Work started at dawn and went on in midsummer until it got dark about eleven o' clock. During the First World War many Barkston boys, including myself, spent their evenings and Saturdays out in the fields with Ward & Dale's engines. Sometimes they were dragging (cultivating) the heavy, hard, yellow clays on the hillsides of Joe Wadkin's farm, or they were stretched across the same hard-baked clays on the rolling expanse of Barkston Gorse. And how those old single-cylinder engines used to bark and shout at their work, and what great half-hundredweight clods were strewn behind the path of the drag! What glorious memories we boys gathered, and what life-long impressions were made! At home, I have fallen asleep to the sound of the engines still at work on the Gorse, and then been awoken by the sound of the clattering tackle coming up West Street at six o'clock in the morning on its way to the next job. A feature of those 1870s singles was the way their meshing cast-steel cog-wheels rang out a tune like that of a mellow peal of steel bells.

A good day's work for a pair of engines was fifteen acres ploughing, or forty when cultivating. A set that worked 3,500 acres in any season had

11. *16 n.h.p. Fowler plough engine, built in the 1870s, on land reclamation work about 1876. Fowler's tackle was used by the Duke of Sutherland to reclaim 2,000 acres of moorland at Strath Ferry, Scotland. This special plough, with stone uprooting hooks, was designed by the Duke.*

done quite well. In their heyday around 1918 Ward & Dale sent out bills to farmers for something like 70,000 acres for the season.

One gloriously sunny afternoon in October 1971, in company with Mr Bill Harmston, a former John Fowler representative, I went to Bonner House, an old people's home in Sleaford, in order to see the late Bill Key, then ninety-two years old and a one-time Ward & Dale plough-set foreman. Both men had worked together before the First World War, and their talk of old times was stirring. To Bill Key the steam-ploughing times had been the best days of his life. Afterwards, Bill Harmston and I walked a hundred yards down the road and stood in the gateway of Ward & Dale's former yard in Mareham Lane. Bill was silent for a few moments. He then said to me: 'I remember coming out of here in the spring of 1910, steering the second engine of a set going south to the Threekingham road. Old Billy Dale stood over there watching us go out, and just as the engine got on to the road, he signalled to the driver to stop. He called me over to him and said, "Never again, Billy, put an engine into such a stunt lock, because it puts great strain on the boiler." That was how the firm was run.

DREDGING PONDS AND LAKES

Cable-type steam-plough engines are ideal for taking mud from the beds of expanses of water, both large and small. All that is required is to place an engine on either side, substitute a mud scoop for the land plough, and everything is ready to start work. Plough engines have always helped the farmer or landowner in this way and at least one contractor still undertakes this work commercially.

The mud scoops are steel boxes with an automatic flap door that shuts the rear end during the actual dredging pull, when about three tons of mud are hauled out. For the engine crews, mud dredging is the filthiest of all jobs done by steam ploughs.

The engine shown in plate 87 is one of a pair that Mr Claud Banham bought in 1934 for £400 complete with all the ploughing gear, and with everything in first-class condition. He then took a team of his own men and drove the engines and tackle 150 miles from Chaddleworth in Berkshire to his home at Runhill in Norfolk.

LAND RECLAMATION IN ITALY AND GERMANY

In his boyhood, Benito Mussolini was once very much impressed by watching a British-built steam engine threshing in Italy. He seems to have retained his steam interests, for when in 1932/4 he drained and reclaimed the Pontine Marshes, some fifty sets of steam-ploughing tackle were used for the work. The majority of the engines were of German make, big twin-cylinder superheated machines, well suited for the heavy task in hand. The English side comprised one set of outsize 'Superba' type, four sets of the big Z7 class, and one small set of DD class 8 n.h.p. single-cylinder engines, all under the personal supervision of Mr Charles Fowler from Leeds. In addition, Mr Fowler also had one set of German tackle working for him.

From earliest times the 290 square miles of marsh, now the Agro Pontino, had been a notorious area of malarial swamp, bush and intermittent rough pasture. Mussolini drained the land, cleared the wild scrub and the trees. New farmhouses were built, some of them from timber felled on the marsh itself, several hundred families were settled on what had previously been a watery wilderness, and the five news towns of Latina, Sabuadia, Pontina, Aprilia and Pomezia were built.

The two huge 25-tons German plough engines shown in plate 93 are engaged upon a rearrangement of various layers of soil in order to bring a fertile layer of sand to the top. In a rather involved and expensive process, the original layer of peat was partly removed from the site and partly buried deeper down in the place of the sand that was finally left on the top as a cropping surface. This reclamation work took place at Ramsloh near Oldenburg, between Bremen and Emden, on low-lying ground drained by the river Weser. Messrs Ottomeyer, deep-ploughing and levelling contractors of Bad Pyrmont, thirty miles south-west of Hanover, carried out the contract in this instance.

The general use of cable-type steam ploughs was as widespread in Germany as in England. At first the Germans bought Fowler's steam ploughs. Then, around the 1890s, they began to build their own engines and, like the British, they made strong engines with plenty of metal in them. In one main respect German practice differed from British, in that whilst Britain went in almost universally for compound engines, the Germans stuck to the idea of two-cylinder single-expansion engines using superheated steam at a fairly high pressure.

12. *The Darby Walking Digger of 1878. This strange contraption, built by W. & S. Eddington of Chelmsford, represents an imaginative but unrewarding attempt by Mr T. C. Darby of Pleshey Lodge near Chelmsford to emulate, in iron, the subtle limb actions of twelve men digging with hand forks. Pivotted road wheels permitted broadside running (as here) in the field.*

13. *Early Fowler traction engine threshing near Malton, North Yorkshire, 1880, with a gang of threshermen and women working with a Leeds-built engine and a Marshall drum. A peculiarity is the double row of staggered strakes on the hind wheel of the engine, a feature that indicates its early age of construction.*

Some idea of the extent to which agricultural steam engines were used in Germany may be gathered from the fact that as early as 1882 there were 6,170 farms in Germany upon which steam engines were employed for threshing or ploughing. In 1907 steam ploughs did work on no less than 2,990 German farms, and even as late as 1933 the steam plough engine was seen on 1,393 farms there. It is estimated, too, that 994 plough engines still remained intact in the year 1933.

EARLY STEAM THRESHING

For many thousands of years man has used as food the grains of wheat, barley, rye and oats, which are the seeds of specialised grasses. When man had coarser feeding habits it is possible that, like baboons in Africa today, he merely plucked off and ate the complete seeded heads of wild grasses. During his first agricultural days, man took the worthwhile grasses and by selection and cultivation improved upon them. By rubbing the ripe heads between the palms of his hands, and blowing away the husks with his mouth, he separated the grains of corn. When man's agriculture became more extensive, he beat out the grain by treading the headed straw under the feet of animals, or by beating it with special sticks called flails. On windy days he threw up into the air the mixed results and allowed the breeze to blow away the husks and chaff on winnowing floors. The threshing machine merely incorporated by mechanical revolutions, shakings, sievings and the wind from fan blowers what had formerly been done by the primitive methods outlined above.

In 1786 Andrew Meikle, a Scotsman, conceived and constructed the first practicable threshing machine, which had a fast-revolving beater drum which rubbed the grain from the husks. By 1820 a fair number of these threshers were at work, mostly inside barns. The small ones were hand-driven and the larger types required horses that walked continuously round and round drawing a pole that turned the wheels of the machinery.

No sooner had it been proved in the 1840s what a big advantage it was to use a steam engine to drive these threshers, than the engine-builders set to work, and by the 1850s they had produced more powerful portable engines, together with larger threshing machines mounted on wheels. This move revolutionised farm threshing, because it set the trend for doing the job outside the barn in the stackyard beside the corn ricks.

Whereas a good flailman could thresh just under two sacks of wheat in a day, the steam outfit with nine men and a boy produced about seventy sacks of better-dressed grain in the same time. Moreover, the straw was now put into its own stack in the stackyard at the same operation.

OLD-TIME STEAM THRESHERMEN

The men who worked the steam engines and the threshing machines in days gone by were just as interesting as the machinery. In plate 20, which shows *Progress* threshing at Syston, Lincolnshire, there appear several characters well worth a mention.

Dick Bradley, the bearded driver, lived in the stone-built East Lodge of Syston Park. He had driven the engine for many years and was most likely in charge of her when she ran away in 1894 on the Poultry Yard Hill above the kitchen gardens in Syston Park, killing the young steersman. Dick's hobby was bell-ringing with the team of ringers in the belfry under the peal of six bells at Barkston church.

The bearded man looking up from the feed hole in the centre of the drum is Georgie Watson of Barkston. He was a part-owner of the Clayton, Shuttleworth & Co. threshing tackle based at Barkston; he normally drove the portable engine that went with it. On this occasion the Thorold Estate at Syston had hired Georgie's drum and elevator or jackstraw to go with their Tuxford engine at the Grange Farm. Georgie was an alert bright-eyed man who, when in charge of the Barkston tackle, always paid the closest attention to all that went on. His dialect was broad Lincolnshire and to him water was always 'watter'. He was on threshing terms with all the Barkston farmers, except old Montague Morley whose little red-brick house and farmyard was at the bottom of West Street, and with whom he had fallen out before my time. My father used to talk of some bother there had been when Morley's fowls had got into Watson's garden and pecked out the greens, but I am not certain about the facts of it all. In consequence, Montague Morley hired an outside threshing contractor who came to him with a green-boilered traction engine threshing tackle. Up to about 1922, when Watson's Clayton portable finally broke down, this was about the only modern tackle seen in the village.

Harry Watson of Barkston stands on the left of the drum with his hand on a sack of pulse, or chaff-like pieces of broken straw. He was a poor relation of Georgie, but worked with him on the Clayton set as the drum-feeder. Harry did this job consistently until the set ceased work. I have known occasions when they were threshing and Harry let too much of a sheaf drop unlittered into the drum, causing the machine to steady up sharply with a decided 'er-yumph', much to the annoyance of Georgie standing behind the engine firebox. He would stand aside, shake his head and wave his clenched fist in the air as a warning to Harry to be more careful in future. Georgie was a keen Baptist who went each Sunday afternoon to the little stone cottage in Barber's Row that had been made into a chapel.

Harry Watson was a regular attending tenor in the church choir with a place in the men's stalls above my stand in the boys' row at the front. I well remember how Harry loved to emphasise the alleluia parts. Many's the time, too, that I have seen Harry coming up the village street after a day's threshing, carrying his plaited-straw food basket slung across his shoulder, and with his face as black as that of any sweep. He was always a quiet, pleasant man, quite free from grumbles of any kind.

Alongside Harry, looking sideways at the camera, stands Billy Watson, also of Barkston. He was an unmarried, simple-minded, harmless fellow, who always trotted to and from his work. As a result of this oddity he was known about the village as 'Billy on the Trot'. In this scene it rather looks as if Billy had the least-wanted job of being in what was called the 'pult hole', or place under the far end of the drum where all the little bits of broken straw, husks and barley awns fell to the ground. 'Pult' was evidently a Lincolnshire corruption of the word 'pulse', meaning the odds and ends of straw and chaff. It would be Billy's dusty, dirty task to rake out the pults on to large pieces of sacking spread on the ground. He then had to lug the loads on his back to the stable chaff-house fifty yards away. As the exhaust wind of the drum blowers escaped with the pults, the area

14. *Burrell pilot steerage engine threshing around 1885. Agricultural engineman Charlie Shearman is the driver on this lovely old chain-drive engine built by Charles Burrell of Thetford in the late 1870s. This photograph was taken at Saffords Farm, Great Gransden, in Cambridgeshire. Sheaf corn was being led directly from stooks in the field to the threshing machine, an operation that was known as 'leading and threshing'.*

was smothered with blowing dust all day. Quite naturally, it usually happened that somebody of Billy's limited intellectual capacity was given the pult-hole job. But despite all the rough work associated with steam threshing, those were grand days and I count myself fortunate in having had the experience of some of those times.

THE LAST YEARS OF STEAM THRESHING

It was during the early 1920s that the encroaching motor tractor began to stand before the drum instead of the more endearing old traction engine. The term 'drum' has been used to describe a threshing machine, because that was the Lincolnshire term that I always used to hear. In some counties it was called a 'box', a 'machine' or a 'mill', and the latter description was used extensively in Scotland.

The drum seen in plate 79 is quite a modern one, capable of threshing up to seventy quarters of grain in a day, or 140 sacks. All corn used to be sold by the quarter, which is a dry measure based on the bushel, and there

were eight bushels in a quarter. The weight of a quarter varied according to the variety of grain. The recognised weights per quarter were: oats 336 lb, barley 448 lb, wheat 500 lb, and beans 532 lb. The weighing machine beside the corn-delivery end of the drum was set to weigh one sack of corn, or half a quarter. It was hard work for a cornman to carry away on his back, or sometimes up steps into a horse cart, one sack at a time, the corn that spouted so fast from the drum. A sack of beans weighed no less than 266 lb and not all men could stand up to this carrying job. After making due allowances for the yield of any particular crop, an average day's threshing in the 1920s produced around thirteen tons of wheat.

Threshing, like steam cultivation, was usually done by a contractor who provided the machinery, as well as the engine-driver and a drum-feeder man. The farmer found the coal (about four hundredweights a day) and the water, and apparently in some counties he also fed the contractor's men at the farmhouse table from breakfast to tea. In the Kesteven Division of Lincolnshire the contractor's charge in 1923 was £3 a day plain, without the farmer finding either beer or meals of any kind.

Whilst steam cultivation was in progress, the farmer often walked over the work and noted whether everything was being done to his satisfaction. And some farmers had rather exacting requirements! At the

15. *Lincoln-built Clayton, Shuttleworth & Co threshing tackle at work about 1890 for farmer Henry Smith of Cropwell Bishop, near Nottingham. The engine, which with its two boiler-mounted simple acting cylinders and front steerage represents the makers' first attempts to build a traction engine for threshing work, is either No 8864 (1868), or No 9338 (1869), both of which were bought new by Mr Smith. Note the water boy with two pails hung from the yoke on his shoulders, and the sheaf tied with straw bands in the foreground, indicating that binders had not come into general use.*

time of threshing, too, the farmer would keep an eye upon what was happening. On one occasion an elderly farmer, Joe Wadkin, came upon the scene when we were using the 1860s Clayton, Shuttleworth & Co. portable tackle. He asked Georgie Watson to go over to the straw stack with him. From the stack he drew several straws and running his fingers down the headed ends he found, as he no doubt expected, that he could feel a number of grains still left in the husks. The old drum was feeling its fifty years of service.

During the years 1922 and 1923, when I worked on John Rilett's farm, we used a threshing set, which belonged to a contractor named Harris who lived at Woodnook on the south side of Grantham, to do our bit of threshing, usually about October. The engine was a Foster single-cylinder type with her front wheels set back a little under her smokebox, Foster fashion. She was a smooth-running engine driven by a young man named Jack Rudd, who lodged at a house in West Street for the eight months' threshing season. It was usually my job to look after the pult hole and carry the pults into the barn or the stable chaff-house, with the water-carrying job thrown in for good luck. Fortunately, the cast-iron horse-trough pump was only thirty yards or so from the engine, but nevertheless I never had a free minute.

John Rilett, my boss, was hard up, but old Mr Headley, who had taken the Manor Farm just after the war finished in 1918, was even more short of money. He asked my boss to loan me for three days threshing at his Beck Hovels Buildings half way to Barkston Gorse Farm. Headley's crops were decidedly poor and we threshed some very poor-quality corn. There was as much of thistles as of wheat and the white thistledown blew away from the drum like a warm snowstorm, covering all the oily parts of the Foster engine in snowy fluff. The poor old farmer, who went bankrupt shortly afterwards, had provided only a limited amount of coal and by 3 p.m. on the last day Jack Rudd shut off steam and said: 'That's the lot, until I get some coal!' Some men cut slices of plug tobacco, filled their pipes and stood around smoking and talking. After a few minutes, however, one or two of the softer-hearted men, taking pity upon old Headley, thought that we should try and finish somehow. Close by was the Fox Covert, a roughish bit of hawthorn cover for foxes and rabbits, and when somebody suggested that we could gather enough dry firewood there to keep the engine going for another hour or so, everybody went 'sticking' for the engine. We hummed our way through the last sheaves burning dry brushwood and a few broken-up pieces of hedge rail.

A few years later Mr Harris, the owner of the threshing tackle, also got caught up in the great trade depression of the 1920s. Besides owning a steam threshing set, he also had a pair of comparatively new J. & H. McLaren compound plough engines that were sold at his Woodnook sale for a mere song.

BOILER EXPLOSIONS

Nothing more frightful could happen to any steam engine than the sudden bursting of its boiler; yet few engine-drivers gave that possibility a second thought. Contributory causes of the early explosions were the driver's allowing the water to get too low or nonchalantly screwing down the safety valves in order to provide some extra power. But the main fault lay in the use of wrought iron, which had a tendency to groove and also to crack along lines of boiler or firebox rivets.

The Bessemer process for the mass production of steel was invented in 1856, and boilermakers began to replace iron with this tougher metal from about 1870 onwards. During the 1860s boiler pressures had gone up from about 50 lb to 100 lb per square inch. By 1900 pressures of 150 lb were common, but by this time the steel boilers were manufactured in a superior manner.

During the era of wrought-iron boilers several threshing engines blew themselves inside out, often killing one or two men and injuring others about the stackyard. In those instances where the firebox crown-plate blew in, the downward rush of steam had sufficient force to lift the whole engine off its wheels and then let it drop down again on its side.

Plough engines, too, produced several loud bangs. Known cracks in boiler or firebox plates caused the deaths of at least two Lincolnshire boilersmiths who were sent out to caulk up the leaks. According to a tale related many years ago, in the early 1870s a steam-cultivation contractor named Henry Yates of Grantham sent out a young boilersmith to caulk a firebox corner fracture on one of his plough engines working at Burton Coggles. The foreman of the set advised lowering the high boiler pressure; but the smith said that he wanted to get back to Grantham Fair, and he set about the job. Whilst he was hammering, a piece of plate blew clean out of the fractured corner. The impact and blast was so violent that the man's dying body was blown fifty yards. The steel caulking tool that the man had been using was slung, like a bullet, into the next field where it fell upon a heap of straw from which a thatcher's man was drawing straight straw into yelms.

When the Board of Trade enquiry was held to look into the boiler explosion shown in plate 54, several interesting facts came to light. On the day of the explosion, the steam-ploughmen had started work at 3 a.m. Just before 8.30 a.m. it was necessary to stop the cultivator beside engine No 2909 in order to splice a rope, and the three men involved were carrying out this work only five yards away from the amidships part of the boiler.

16. East Anglian threshing about 1890. The elegant curved-spoke flywheel, the wooden-rimmed road wheels and the two very heavy speed governor balls on this ancient Ransome portable engine suggest that she was made in the 1870s. The drum, too, is an early model from which the straw is being carried by the two men on the left.

This was unfortunate, because when the thirty-seven years old boiler, built for a working pressure of 100 lb but which had been lifted up to 120 lb, exploded, the men were right in the path of the scalding water and pieces of flying metal. The safety valves were blowing off at 120 lb when the boiler burst.

The pair of engines had changed hands once or twice during the previous two years, and the boiler insurances had lapsed thirteen months earlier. In 1911 a hydraulic test of 180 lb had been carried out by a boiler inspector without the outside lagging being removed. This man, who apparently was not sure about the thickness of the worn boiler-plate, made certain entries in lead pencil on his form, so as not to preclude alterations that he might wish to make later on. In 1912 the engines passed into new ownership and the same inspector was told by his company to make an approach asking for a thorough test to be carried out. But, due to various circumstances, the boilers were not insured, neither were any thorough inspections made.

After the explosion, it was found that in addition to a long crack, in many places the wrought-iron boiler-plate, originally three-eighths of an inch thick, was worn down to less than a quarter of an inch in thickness. It was ruled that the owners had failed to have the boiler properly examined and the Board of Trade Surveyor considered that 'justice of the case will be met by a £50 fine'.

17. *Fowler experimental eight-furrow turn-over plough being demonstrated at the 1894 Royal Agricultural Society of England's show at Cambridge. It was hoped to supersede the balance plough with something less clumsy to handle at the ends, but this example proved impractical and the balance plough was never displaced.*

THE HAND OF THE LAW

Traction-engine owners always nursed a grievance that the laws of the land were against them. This was decidedly so; but agricultural users did enjoy certain dispensations. They were, for instance, exempted under the Locomotives Act of 1861 from paying road tolls. Like everyone else, however, they were obliged under the Locomotives on Roads Act of 1865, or the Red Flag Act, to have a flagman sixty yards in front of every engine, or the first of two plough engines on the move, and they had to conform to the general 2 m.p.h. speed limit in towns and villages, and a top speed of four miles an hour upon the open road. An onerous bugbear until 1878 was the power of local authorities to prohibit steam engines from passing along turnpike roads, except between midnight and 6 a.m. This meant that in certain instances agricultural steam machinery could move only during those night hours and some drivers were fined for being on a turnpike shortly after six o'clock as they neared the end of their journey.

The Highways and Locomotives Act of 1878 removed the need for a red flag, but a man still had to walk twenty yards in advance of each engine, mainly to look after any horses that were likely to become frightened. This act also gave power to county authorities to vary their byelaws concerning any annual registration they wished to impose on engines used within their territory. The maximum registration fee was £10.

Compulsory registration of all traction engines was introduced under the Locomotives Act of 1898. But the owners of agricultural engines received the concession of a nominal payment of 12½p only for the annual registration. Other users paid a minimum of £10 each year.

COUNTRY TOWN FAIRS AND VILLAGE FEASTS

Although no stretch of imagination could make the ornate showman's engine into an agricultural machine, this type of engine did once play a useful and significant part in providing jollity for thousands of people who worked on the land. The annual fair in the nearest market town was taken for granted by farmworkers and their womenfolk as an occasion for letting their hair down. It was at many of these country fairs, too, that farmers hired their unmarried horsemen for the ensuing year, whilst at the same time their wives bargained with girls for a year's work as maids in the farmhouse. According to my father, it was the custom at the Grantham May Fair for the men to stand on one side of the High Street near the Angel Hotel, with the girls lined up on the pavement on the west side. The bargain was bound by acceptance of the hirer's shilling. This old custom, known to us as 'going into service', petered out shortly after the end of the war in 1918, and from the 1930s the showman's engine, too, was seen no more down below in the Market Place.

Early each May we had at Barkston a one-day midweek club feast that was associated with the annual celebrations of the men who belonged to the Blue Club Sick Fund. The jollifications were held on the three-cornered village green outside the Stag Inn. I am speaking, of course, of the 1912-1916 period which I can recall personally. There was always one showman's engine present. Whilst generating electricity for the lights on the roundabouts, this engine stood on the then little used roadway at the west side of the green, but now widened and part of the busy A607. A ride on the horses or cockerels on the roundabouts cost ½p and, when we had spent our money, there was always the massive and magnificent engine to stand and gaze at in awe. From about 1916 the parish council refused to rent the green to any of the travelling showmen, due to the scare at that time over raiding German zeppelins seeing lights on the ground. The last wartime feast was held in the paddock of John Rilett's Pear Tree Farm, when the engine and all other activity stopped at the approach of dusk in the evening.

The Foster engine *Prince Bert,* shown in plate 52, may never have attended our Feast, but one day about 1914 she did stand outside the Stag Inn in the early afternoon with a long load of fairground equipment whilst her crew and the truckmen had a pint or two to fortify themselves for the road forward to Lincoln.

---

18. (Top right) *Steam ploughing engine passing through Westgate in Peterborough. The iron lids of every tool or spud box would clatter as this 12-tons unsprung Fowler engine, a Single of the 1870s, passed thunderously over the rough-riding cobbles of this as yet (about 1890-1900) motorless town. The crew, too, would have been seen bouncing up and down, but to them that was nothing. Worse trouble had been the recent knocking off of a safety valve (there is only one valve in use) and a broken flywheel when the plough had been pulled up too close to this, the second engine of a pair belonging to Messrs Hills, contractors from Dogsthorpe nearby.*

19. (Lower right) *Accident to a plough engine about 1900 at Navenby near Lincoln. Whilst in the ownership of Ward & Dale of Sleaford, this Fowler Single No 1165 of 1868 ran away down the hill between the village and the GNR station. The friction band drive to one hind wheel had been adjusted the previous day, but it slipped on the hill. On the left is Bill Clark, foreman of the set.*

20. *William Tuxford & Sons traction engine threshing on the Thorold Estate at Syston, Lincolnshire, about 1898. This is a copy of a most interesting framed photograph that has hung for many years in the cottage home of the Storer family at Welby near Grantham. Boston-built 'Progress' (1872), driven by Dick Bradley of Syston, had the unusual features of chain drive, volute steel springs incorporating india-rubber pads, a water tank under her smokebox, two flywheels, and stub axles at the near or front end; the old engine also ran tender first. Sir Henry Thorold, Bart., paid £420 for 'Progress' when new. This engine was a truly general purpose one, because she hauled coal, threshed, powered a one-engine Fiskin-style roundabout ploughing tackle, cut chaff, and at night sometimes supplied steam to boil pig food.*

21. (Above) *Well sinkers' portable engine at work in 1899 at Church Farm, Thurlby, near Bourne in Lincolnshire. The little engine powered the winch by which the bore of this artesian well was driven down 80ft to underground water that eventually gushed up with a 12 ft head for use on the farm.*

22. (Top right) *1868 Fowler plough engine, south of Lincoln, early 1900s, with a cultivator fitted with sturdy deep rooting tines, here in the act of turning automatically by the pull of the rope from the engine across the field. The engine is Single No 1166, rebuilt after its boiler explosion in 1879.*

23. (Lower right) *Fowler single-cylinder plough engine and turning cultivator, about 1900. The engine, built in 1876, unusually has a steam dome over its firebox. The idea, not followed up, was to take steam from the highly perched dome when the engine was head down on a steep hillside, and so prevent water priming into the cylinder.*

24. (Above) *Lincolnshire folk with their steam engines at Bardney, early 1900s. The Marshall threshing engine in front has a wooden front axle, whilst the 'coffee-pot' Fowler plough engine behind sports an 'improved' style of smokebox door. The tall man met an untimely death when, whilst steering a cultivator one foggy day, the implement arrived at the pulling engine, mysteriously upside down.*

25. (Top right) *Threshing in 1902 at Harris Farm, Castor, near Peterborough, with an 1880 portable. This engine is a rare type made by Farmer, Robey Brown & Co of Gainsborough. The sloping gauge glass above the driver's hand indicated the water level in the boiler, whilst the curved iron bar pillow above the cylinder formed the rest for the chimney when lowered for travelling. Bob Gibbons, the owner's 3-year-old son, stands on the tool-box; he died in 1975 in Peterborough Hospital.*

26. (Lower right) *Steam roller at work in Somerset, late 1890s. This single-cylinder Basingstoke-built Wallis & Steevens roller was then operated by W. W. Buncombe. In order not to frighten the pony, all movement would stop until after the farmer's wife had passed safely in her gig. Waistcoat watch-chains were very fashionable at that time with country roadmakers.*

27. (Above) *Steam threshing outfit at work on a prairie harvest field about 1905 near Lisbon, North Dakota, USA. This illustration shows how the North American engines, with crossed belts, stood well back from their grain separators, as threshing machines were called out west. The separator man stands high upon his machine and he was most likely the owner and the boss of this outfit. Behind him on the right rears the pipe of the windstacker that blew the straw out on to a cone-shaped pile. The usual engine crew consisted of an engineer, a fireman, a water-tank man, and a flunkey who helped the fireman with supplies of straw, wood or coal for fuel.*

28. (Right) *Benjamin Holt steam tractor ploughing in California, USA, 1904. Direct steam traction was greatly developed for use on the immense cornlands of North America and this was the American and Canadian way of doing land cultivation. Our British cable-style tackle was little used there. This illustration is one of the earliest showing caterpillar tracks, which have become so common today on many farm tractors powered by oil engines.*

31. (Above) *Mole draining in the Evesham area, about 1905. The firm of Bomfords used an 8 n.h.p. Fowler plough engine, in conjunction with a separate auxiliary engine, for handling a mole-drainer implement. By taking steam from the plough engine boiler and using the little engine on the cart at the rear to haul back the empty drainer, the work could be done without having a second engine across the field.*

29. (Top left) *Aveling & Porter traction engine with a saw bench, early 1900s. Tree logs have been brought into the farm paddock ready for sawing up into lumber for farm requirements. The smaller arms of the trees and the cut-offs would be sawn off into logs for the farmhouse fire. Aveling & Porter always fixed their rampant-horse motif on the front of each engine built in their works at Rochester in Kent.*

30. (Lower left) *Three-tons single-cylinder Garrett tractor No 25399 hauling a plough in 1905. Garretts thought that this little engine would solve the problems of direct-traction ploughing on British soils. But a still rather big engine and two men convey an impression of a weighty and labour-intensive device for three-furrow ploughing. The spineless chain haulage must have led to awkward turning at the ends, and wide un-ploughed headlands.*

32. (Above) *Pamplin Bros yard and works at Braughing, Hertfordshire, about 1906. Pamplins were well-known East Anglian steam cultivation contractors, whose main depot was at Cherry Hinton near Cambridge. The man sitting in the pony trap is Joe Sparrow, who was an outrider or agent for working tackles. It is said that whenever arguments ran hot about the respective merits of single-cylinder engines, compounds or single-crank compounds, Joe Sparrow always chipped in with, 'You can't beat the old doubles'. He was, of course, harking back to the old times when as a young man he had been in charge of a set of the 1860 period two-cylinder Fowler engines.*

33. (Left) *Ruston (Lincoln) portable threshing near Holbeach, Lincs: summer or early autumn activity seventy years ago at one of the flat fenland farmsteads of south Lincolnshire. The long straw of fen-grown wheat, the old-fashioned drum with two corn-delivery spouts only, the calm face of the old engine-driver, and his wicker dinner basket by the coal-cart wheel all add to the attractiveness of this photograph.*

34. (Above) *Large steam outfit threshing from stooks on the prairie near Dauphin, Manitoba, Canada, in 1906. These travelling threshing outfits required about ten horse-drawn 'bundle' wagons to supply the separator with sheaves. Work started at 6 a.m. and went on till dark. The bigger separators of the 1920s could thresh a hundred tons of wheat in a day. This photograph was taken by Sir Edmund Walker, General Manager of the Canadian Bank of Commerce, during a tour of the prairie provinces.*

35. (Top right) *Plough engine in a punt, 1906. By the appearance of the hedgerows, this trial of Fowler cultivating machinery, intended for the low canalised farmlands in Trinidad, was carried out in England. The picture shows how versatile and obliging Fowlers were in their attempts to satisfy all potential steam-minded customers.*

36. (Lower right) *Young Charles E. Hooker had so much steam in his blood that his father's 1874 Aveling & Porter one-speed threshing engine No 1019 'Dandy Jim' was turned out to haul home his bride, himself and the principal guests from his wedding at St James's church, Egerton, Kent, at Easter 1906. The Hookers were haulage, rolling and threshing contractors, and Charles died aged 91, and his funeral service was held on 7th March 1975 in Ditton church near Maidstone.*

37. (Above) *Threshing in Russia in 1908 with Clayton, Shuttleworth & Co. machinery. Seventy years ago the whole world was buying British agricultural steam tackle. The Clayton type of spark arrester chimney top, the pile of wood fuel with Clayton's man beside it, the low-bodied Russian horse wagons, and the labour force of at least 27 men and women should be noted. Five forkers are required to pass the straw between the elevator and the somewhat remote straw stack.*

38. (Top right) *Case 110 h.p. ploughing engine at work in Oklahoma, USA. This postcard, mailed in 1909 to Mr W. E. Gardner of Iowa by his aunt Cora, was sent 'to show how they farm in this country'. Jerome Increase Case, founder of the Racine firm that made the engine, was known as the Threshing Engine King of the USA. The gang-type plough is equipped with multiple rows of sharp disc wheels that first cut the soil, and then turn it over.*

39. (Lower right) *Direct-traction ploughing with a Wallis & Steevens light steam tractor in 1909: a bright but ultimately unsuccessful attempt at direct traction, using the unique arrangement of a hinged plough body at either end of the little engine. In this view the engine is moving backwards, steered by the ploughman whose wheel turns the front axle on the engine. Straight steering must have been a problem with this trial outfit.*

41. (Top right) *Threshing in Turkey, 1909, with an English engine. As in Russia (plate 37), the gang is a large one, but it doubtless includes sickle reapers, corn leaders, and threshers, as well as those who just wanted to have their photographs taken. Hot sunshine is a feature of harvest on the Turkish plateau, making it necessary to shade the driver by bending sheets of corrugated iron over his head.*

42. (Lower right) *Steam tractor carting hay, 1909. This is another Wallis & Steevens engine trying unsuccessfully to outdo the horse, this time in the hayfield. The engine could do the job, but considering the trouble involved providing coal and water there was no advantage. Moreover, a pair of horses in a hay cart did not require a separate boy or man to drive them whilst loading up in the field.*

40. (Below) *Steam threshing in France about 1910. The domed and small flywheeled engine beside a huge barn with its long sloping roof and a grape vine stretched along its wall present a typically French scene. The crop has little straw whilst the chaff is being pipe blown into the barn. Traction engine and machine were made by the Sociêtê Français de Material Agricole et Industriel of Vierzon in Champagne.*

45. (Above) *A Mann's steam tractor on trial in 1910. The question was whether this 4¾-tons 20 i.h.p. high-pressure and high-speed compound engine could drive a large thresher (54in beater drum) as well as a 5-7 n.h.p. portable or traction engine nearly twice the tractor's weight. The cornman is using an elevator that raises the sack to shoulder height. Note the beautifully built round corn rick with its superb thatching.*

43. (Top left) *The farmworkers' beer arrives by steam wagon, about 1910. During the years 1905 to 1920 many village pubs had their beer delivered in wooden barrels by steam wagons, such as this Foden five-tonner No 1840. Foden wagons, with their free steaming boilers and high-speed engines of great strength, enjoyed a fine reputation with the men who drove them.*

44. (Lower left) *The main personality of this group of south Lincolnshire threshing men at Morton, near Bourne, is the boy who carried water to the engine. He stands with the engine boiler feed-pump behind his head and the feed water-tub below his left hand. His two buckets are on the ground, but the wood and chain yoke, by which he carried them, is slung across his shoulders. It is a Garrett engine.*

46. (Right) *Threshing in the Rostoff district of Russia, about 1911, with a Garretts of Leiston engine. Note that there is top-level supervision, which in Britain would probably have been left to the cornman or engine-driver. The man on the right is feeding straw into the furnace of the engine specially adapted as a straw burner. The inverted cone at the base of the chimney is a spark arrester, essential with a straw-burning engine.*

47. (Below) *Steam sawing: a rural summer scene in Earl Fitzwilliam's Milton Park near Peterborough about 1910. The old Burrell portable engine has wooden wheels, and the three-wheeled water-cart has an estate-made look about it. Sounds such as the steady huffing of the engine and the short sharp screams of the circular saw would emanate from this activity. The product is firewood logs in readiness for winter.*

48. *Reversible disc harrows made by Fowlers. Ploughing and cultivating were the main tasks that plough engines performed for farmers, but some harrowing was also undertaken. Where the land was strewn with dried clods, a disc harrow was used to slice the lumps into smaller pieces and produce a finer tilth in which seeds could germinate and take root more easily.*

49. (Right) *John Fowler's steam plough works at Leeds in 1912. Although Fowlers made quite a wide range of steam-powered machinery, agricultural engines for threshing and cultivation always formed a large part of their output. The two partly erected plough engines in the left and right foreground are Nos 13291 and 13290. These works, opened in 1860, have been run recently by the Marshall-Fowler Organisation, but were closed early in 1974 when production was concentrated at Marshalls modernised works in Gainsborough.*

50. (Below) *A 1910 view of Ward & Dale's yard at Sleaford. Here are the cream of the steam cultivation engines and men of Lincolnshire. Foremen of sets and drivers stand on the engines, all Singles built in the 1860s and 1870s, and a boilersmith stands in the wheelbarrow. The handcart, known as Sam Clay's chariot, was used by the foremen on Monday mornings to take oil and stores to Sleaford station, before these men set out to join their tackles scattered about the countryside.*

51. (Right) *Three Avery 30 brake-horsepower undermounted steam tractors breaking prairie sod for wheatlands in Canada about 1912. Each engine is pulling ten Cockshutt ploughs with soil packers behind the front and the rear plough sets. The total width of work was 35 feet and the three engines ploughed 56 acres in a day.*

52. (Below) *Fun and games for farm children were associated with resplendent engines like 1911 8 n.h.p. Foster compound No 12620 'Prince Bert'. Showmen's engines, glittering with polished copper and brass, hauled roundabouts and other amusements on an annual round of fairs and feasts. This photograph was taken in 1912 at Swadlincote, Derbyshire, and shows the engine in position to generate electricity for the exotic lighting.*

53. (Above) *Two Manns lightweight tractors, with water tanks over their hind wheels, hauling four-furrow ploughs about 1912. Manns of Leeds unsuccessfully tried this type of steam tractor in an attempt to check the development of the motor tractor.*

54. (Below) *Boiler explosion at Benniworth, Lincs. This plough engine was 1876 14 n.h.p. Fowler single-cylinder No 2909. The foreman died from his injuries, whilst the driver and cultivator steersman were severely injured. The explosion was attributed to a 26in crack in a boiler plate.*

57. (Above) *Side-drum plough engine: cultivating in Cambridgeshire about 1916. This rare Burrell 'Universal' type engine, single crank compound No 2889, was built in 1907 at Thetford. The set was owned by George Flack, a contractor living at Orwell, and his three men from left to right are: Stan Williams, 'Shorter' George Gill, and Ernie Fuller. There is a short length of wire hanging on the lamp bracket ready for use should it be necessary to splice a broken rope.*

55. (Top left) *Steam-hauled Sunday-school outing in 1914. Normally this Ransome threshing engine was at work on farms around Haddenham in Buckinghamshire. On this occasion, however, she had been selected by the Green family, who were Baptists, to take their Sunday-school party on its annual outing to Whiteleaf Cross, an ancient mark on the chalk hillside above Princes Risborough. Mr Roland B. Green still proudly rides about Haddenham on 'Pentland Queen', his 1927 12 tons Fowler roller No 17501.*

56. (Lower left) *A threshing and chaff cutting team at Sutton near Castor, Peterborough, October 1916. The unthreshed crop comes out of the top door of the barn and the straw falls into the chaff cutter, placed broadside on. The bagged chaff had to be carried up the ladder and pitched through another top door over the chaff house. The addition of a chaff cutter made threshing a much harder job for the engine. The central figure is Bob Gibbons who also appears in plate 25.*

59. (Above) *Fowler-Goode tandem compound plough engine. That there was an ordinary farmer who, by his inventive talent and personal engineering ability, was able to improve upon Fowlers engines, is clearly demonstrated by the fine-looking machine above. Edwin J. Goode of Lodge Farm, Elmdon, in Essex, had found the Fowler Singles heavy on both coal and water, so he modified five pairs of these engines by adding a compound cylinder ahead of the original one. Taken about 1914, this photograph shows a big engine taking some of the mud from its last field along to its next forty-acre stint at Little Chishill in Cambridgeshire.*

58. (Previous page) *A First World War Saturday morning scene of 1917 in St Neots GNR station yard. The engines, all Fowlers except the rear centre Garrett tractor, have brought in the baled straw from nearby farms for forwarding by rail to military depots or camps to provide feed or bedding for army mules and horses. Soldiers not only man the engines, but they also almost overfill the little hackney carriage. Five ministry lady clerks, who checked the deliveries, look down from a loaded wagon. The Fowler TE2 engines, newly built for the Ministry of Munitions, have special gun-winching slant-drive horizontal rope-drums. Neither of them had so far been given a road registration plate.*

60. (Above) *Foden steam wagon setting out in 1917 to gather apples from Mr Mash's orchards. Driver Reid stands on the road: Mrs Reid, her daughter and a friend have their heads covered against the shower of ash from the chimney.*

61. (Below) *Garrett 'Suffolk Punch' steam tractor No 32974 with a four-furrow plough. Garretts built this lightweight in 1917 to counteract the threat to steam from motor tractors. Its boiler pressure was no less than 220 lb per sq in. The box below the chimney houses the superheater.*

62. (Above) *Trussing straw in the First World War. Soldiers of the Forage Department of the Army Service Corps using a Burrell single-crank compound general-purpose engine with a Ruston straw-baler. Men with agricultural or traction-engine backgrounds were best suited for this work, but often only the engine-driver was really experienced. T. T. Boughton & Sons, threshing and timber-hauling contractors of Amersham Common, Bucks, provided the army with a number of trained drivers, including Private George Harris, in charge of this engine. On the left is the crane, which also weighed each bale it handled.*

63. (Top right) *Of all the traction or plough engines ever built, for sheer elegance in outline, none surpassed the Fowler BB class ploughers. This is No 15142, built in 1918, and notice how the round shapes blend perfectly. The curved-spoke flywheel is a beautifully placed piece of ironwork. Moreover, these engines were a great success at their work in the fields. The first of the BB engines, designed by a Mr Livesey, came out just before the First World War.*

64. (Lower right) *A Fowler steam plough waits for wheat stooks to be cleared at High Down, Goring, Sussex, about 1918. The special interest of this picture is that it shows a splendid crop of stooked wheat and a compound plough engine together in the same field. The engine, with a plough that has a five-wheel land presser hooked at the rear, has just gone into the field in readiness to begin work immediately the farmer started to lead away the corn sheaves.*

67. (Above) *John Fowler mole drainer implement as used by a pair of cable-type steam plough engines. The 4 inch diameter bullet-shaped snout or mole is 2ft below ground doing its hole-making work. A double purchase pull was obtained by passing the hauling cable round the horizontal sheave wheel at the front. The mole was raised or lowered by turning the handle in the centre of the upper steel beam.*

65. (Top left) *Fowler engine coupled by belt to circular saw. Wintertime threshing would be the main occupation of this engine, but in summer it could be used to saw wood. Long planks rest against the wall, whilst a pile of gate posts can be seen behind the saw bench. What looks like a Cambridgeshire County Council registration plate, required by the act of 1898, is fixed to the side of the tender.*

66. (Lower left) *A threshing contractor has a sale day. A pair of threshing engines lined up ready for the auctioneer and prospective new owners at Baughurst in Hampshire, probably around 1919. The plate on the boiler of the Wallis & Steevens engine gives her owners as H. & J. Kent. The other plate, further back on the hornplate, is her Hampshire County Council registration fixture.*

68. (Above) *Steam plough set built by Aveling & Porter of Rochester, Kent, whose limited output of such engines never approached that of Fowlers. This 1922 photograph shows a complete set of tackle outside Otway House Farm, Pinchbeck, near Spalding. The leading engine, 12 n.h.p No 8890 'Field Marshal Haig', has two ploughs, one for shallow and one for deep work, whilst No 8891 'General Byng' follows with the living van and the water-cart.*

69. (Top right) *Stationary indoor steam engine on a Scottish farm. In Scotland threshing machines were often fixed in barns. This little engine probably dates from the 1880s. It is seen here working in 1924 at Eastfield Farm, Symington, Lanarkshire, where it drove a mill, a corn bruiser or crusher, a chaff cutter and a saw bench. The man is Bob Linton who still takes a keen interest in steam engines.*

70. (Lower right) *Yorkshire Power Farmer light tractor. The Yorkshire Patent Steam Engine Co. of Hunslet, Leeds, built this novel unit in 1924, vainly hoping to beat the encroaching motor tractor. Designed mainly by Mr A. M. Phillips of Letchworth, a rear-mounted rope-drum was incorporated so that pairs of such engines might perform cable cultivation. The crosswise boiler, with a smokebox at either side, is a typical Yorkshire wagon feature.*

71. *Aveling & Porter compound 12 n.h.p. plough engine No 8890 of 1916 'Field Marshal Haig' ploughing during 1923 in the Lincolnshire Fens. Aveling's plough engines were of good appearance, but were noisy in the bevel wheel drive to the rope-drum, and in performance never equalled Fowlers' engines. The right-hand man is Walter Broughton, foreman of this set from 1919 to 1953.*

72. *Steam cultivation in Germany, 1925. Many German firms made cable-style steam ploughs, and this superheated engine is a product of the Borsig Company. It is hauling a turning type spring-tine cultivator. All plough engines have their front wheels set well forward to give a wide angle clearance to the rope, but this engine is exceptional in this respect.*

73. *Threshers' lunch at Cholsey Five Ways, Oxfordshire. Leather leggings and tied-up trousers worn by the older men date this photograph to the early 1920s. With so many sacks already filled, the men are justified in smiling over their out-of-doors meal. I myself have often been a member of similar refreshment parties and know well what happy occasions they were for those taking part. The engine, which has her front end nicely set up in a way that pleased all drivers, is Fowler No 7953 built in 1899 and then owned by R. J. & H. Wilder of Wallingford. She was broken up in the 1930s.*

76. (Above) *Testing Wansford Bridge on the Great North Road (A1) in 1928. Before this newly built bridge was brought into general use, the deflection effects of heavy weights upon it were tested by traction engines and steam rollers belonging to Mr G. Briggs, a steam-power contractor of Stamford nearby. Several of the engines were his steam ploughs, temporarily released from ploughing the land, and Mr Briggs personally supervised the traction-engine side of the operations.*

74. (Top left) *English steam ploughing, April 1927. Although the plough is turning three furrows only, it is quite deep work that is being done here. Farmers required deep ploughs for such deep-rooting crops as potatoes or sugar beet. One look at the heaved-up ground is sufficient to show how well the plough has turned over this hard stubble land left over from the previous autumn. These balance, or anti-balance, ploughs moved quietly across the fields and the gritting of ploughshares in the earth was a pleasant sound to any steersman's ears.*

75. (Lower left) *1928 Foden Agri-tractor. Fodens of Sandbach in Cheshire were rightly famous as builders of first-rate steam wagons, and this engine was their bright idea in the last days of steam construction. It was intended as a light agricultural tractor for direct-style work. The wire-spoked wheels, the 250lb per sq in boiler pressure generated in a water-tube type boiler, and the inclined and enclosed high-speed engine are each all notable features. Only about three were built and most went abroad. A basically similar 'Sun' type tractor intended for road haulage work is preserved by Mr R. H. Crawford of Frithville near Boston, Lincs.*

77. (Above) *Peruvian farewell to British steam ploughs. The management of the Aspillga estate at Cayalti in Peru had been so pleased with the 43 years of outstanding performance obtained from these Fowler plough engines, that their 1928 retirement was marked by this touching ceremony. How wonderful it would have been if every set in the homeland had been played out with a brass band!*

78. (Top right) *Sentinel 'Rhinocerus' steam tractor, a very specialised 12-tons machine made by the Sentinel Wagon Works of Shrewsbury in 1928. Her 88 i.h.p. two-cylinder simple acting engine had stainless steel poppet valves that distributed superheated steam at 275lb pressure. She is seen at work in southern Africa with a six-furrow plough that must have tested her haulage powers to the limit. There was only a narrow market for these last-days-of-steam machines. Water consumption was 60 gallons per acre ploughed and the main tank required refilling after each 4 acres work.*

79. (Lower right) *Threshing barley and baling the straw in the early 1940s. The grey sky and the well wrapped-up men indicate that this was a cold winter's day. The drum feeder is wearing a balaclava ear-flapped cap, as well as an old brass-buttoned soldier's overcoat. The nodding motion of that piece of machinery looking like a horse's head packed the straw down tightly into the trusses before they were tied with wire. Barley straw made good winter feed for horses and cattle.*

80. *Lugging the lumber off the land in 1930 at Ketton Park, Leicestershire. Most standing timber belonged to the village squire, as here; but where a farmer owned his own land, he could sell the mature tall trees that grew in his hedgerows. This big oak or elm butt, mounted on a timber 'drug', is being pulled off grassland in spring by a 1928 5 tons Clayton, Shuttleworth & Co. steam tractor operated by Messrs Rose, timber merchants of North Luffenham.*

81. *Helping to reclaim the Pontine Marshes in 1933. Mussolini was a project man whose major agricultural accomplishment was to drain and cultivate the Pontine Marshes south-east of Rome. This wide expanse of wet scrubby marsh had defied the ancient Romans, but what they could not do with slave labour, Mussolini achieved by steam power. Here we see a Fowler Z7 plough engine with an Italian team. The raised end of the plough can be seen on the other side of the engine chimney.*

82. *This expressive photograph, taken in 1930 at John H. Ogden's Poplars Farm at March in Cambridgeshire, shows a Fowell's of St Ives engine driving a Clayton, Shuttleworth & Co. drum. The straw elevator, with its extra long 35ft trough and a high 30ft lift, was made specially by Mr Ogden himself. Mrs Taylor, the band cutting lady, was a champion hand at the game who could cut the twine close to the knots. In springtime, when there were hundreds of mice in the stacks, she used to come down from the drum at meal times, walk a little way out from the threshing and shake the mice out of her petticoats. Mr Ogden, now 84, is in his shirt sleeves, Harry Sizer is driving the engine, whilst Spot the dog is sniffing under sheaves for mice and rats. The lovely old black carthorse, Whitefoot, is hitched to the corn cart with its rest pole lowered in order to take the weight off the horse's back.*

83. *Crushing roadstone in Aberdeenshire, 1933. Of the many tasks for which steam power was used none was worse than running a rock crusher for the making of roadstone. The engine, whose maker is not known, is coupled by belt to the stone breaker.*

84. *Cultivating at Walton near Peterborough about 1933. The well cared-for plough engine, 1918 Fowler 16n.h.p. BB1 No 15222, owned by George Briggs of Stamford, has just been watered by the farmer's man with his horses harnessed to the tackle's 250-gallon water-cart.*

85. 'The Pathfinder', originally a Foden steam wagon, was cut down to a
tractor by her second owner, Bob Linton, who stands by the smokebox; he
fitted a heavier flywheel and a governor so that she could be used for
driving a threshing mill, as here in 1938 at Edderston Farm, Peebles.

86. One-engine or roundabout steam ploughing at Acton Pits, Sudbury,
Suffolk, 1934. Ransome engine 8722 is coupled by chain drive to the
windlass from which a rope was led down each side of the field, so that by
controlled reversing of the windlass drums, the plough was pulled
alternately from one side to the other. Engine and windlass remained
stationary.

87. *Pond dredging at Great Ellingham, Norfolk, 1935. Mr Alfred Allen, on the left, was the foreman of a set of steam plough engines, owned by Mr Claud Banham, on the right. His BB 14 n.h.p. Fowler compound engine No 14710 of 1917, and its sister on the far side, are dredging the pond of Mr Beals (centre) by a cable-hauled mud scoop. Two thousand cubic yards of black mud were taken from this pond. The spuds or grips on the hind wheel prevented the engine from digging itself into the soft ground.*

88. (Top right) *The closing down sale at Ward & Dale Ltd., Sleaford, March 1939. The two engines in the foreground, BB No 15412 and her partner No 15413, both new in 1919, went for a mere £80. On the extreme left stands a BBS superheated 17 n.h.p. made in 1915, either No 13978 or 13979. They were sold for £68 the pair! Ten two-engine steam cultivation sets, all of them fine compounds and their tackle, changed hands on that sad day.*

89. (Lower right) *Abandoned Z7 plough engines in California. Their last sugar beet furrow drawn, this pair of big Fowlers stand forlorn and forgotten on a weed patch in the Spreckels Sugar Company's yard at Salinas Valley. They were the last of ten engines once owned by that company and were broken up shortly after this photograph was taken in 1942. Note the extra wide wheel rims for overseas service, the huge cylinder blocks and the ends of the superheater element tubes seen through the partly open smokebox door of the near engine.*

90. (Above) *Aveling & Porter threshing engine No 9010, built at Rochester. It was unusual to find a threshing engine on rubbers. Her owner was the late Mr Chris Lambert of Horsmonden, Kent. The Pickering three-ball speed governor fitted to this engine was more sensitive and satisfactory than the Watt type with two heavy iron balls seen on some older engines.*

91. (Top right) *Fowler 10 n.h.p. No 14977 of 1918 threshing at Kirton, Lincolnshire, August 1949, in the last years of steam threshing. The big TE2 engine, with her slant-shaft driven underslung rope-drum, was a First World War Ministry of Munitions engine intended for hauling and winching heavy artillery, but by the time she left the works those needs must have been fulfilled, for she went into agriculture.*

92. (Lower right) *Roundabout ploughing on Romney Marsh, Kent, 1952. McLaren general purpose engine No 112 provides sole power for the two-drum winch wagon. A jointed shaft connects flywheel to winch and the driver has full control from the footplate. The winch road wheels are wedged tight and the wagon is chained to the engine's rear wheel. This roundabout tackle, the last to work in Britain, has been preserved by Commander J. M. Baldock at Liphook, Hamshire.*

93. *Outsize German steam ploughs on land reclamation work in 1971 at Ramsloh. These engines were built in 1953-6 by Wilhelm Ottomeyer of Bad Pyrmont, especially for reclaiming peat land. Here is a tandem pair with both ropes hitched to the plough, and a similar pair is placed at the opposite end of the field. The absence of flywheels allows quick reverse.*

94. *The massive plough being hauled by the two huge engines above. It has only one furrow but digs down no less than 8ft. On the land side it runs on a wide caterpillar track and on the furrow side by a 20ft diameter wheel. A diesel engine on the plough frame provides hydraulic power for steerage.*

95. (Above) *John Patten's sale on 28th June 1960 at Little Hadham, Hertfordshire; the succession of flywheels, cogwheels and chimneys belonging to the eight plough engines after the auction at Hall Farm. The first flywheel belongs to No 15362 'Lion' and the second to No 15363 'Tiger', both AA7s built in 1919. The average price was £240 an engine, ranging from £170 to £320. John Patten, who died in 1960, was the last British steam cultivation contractor.*

96. (Right) *The last steam-plough gang. Six John Patten steamploughmen on the sale day, with BB 16 n.h.p. No 14383 'Prince' and No 14384 'Princess'. The old foreman on the right is not wiping away a tear of regret but was in fact slightly bored with the day's proceedings. All Patten plough engines had 800-yard rope-drums, so essential for the wide fields of this district.*

97. *Dredging the lake in Berkswell Park, near Coventry, 1972. This picture illustrates quite clearly how a pair of plough engines, using a cable-hauled mud scoop, cleared the beds of ponds and lakes. The engine in the foreground is 12 n.h.p. Fowler K7 No 14695, made in 1917, whilst its mate across the water is BB 14 n.h.p. No 13481 of 1913. Both engines were then owned by Construction & Excavation Ltd, of Tettenhall near Wolverhampton. This job took six months.*

Index

Printed by C. I. Thomas & Sons (Haverfordwest) Ltd.,
Press Buildings, Merlins Bridge, Haverfordwest, Pembrokeshire.